Hikaru's Toy Troubles

A Transportation Engineering Story

Written by the Engineering is Elementary Team

Illustrated by Ross Sullivan-Wiley

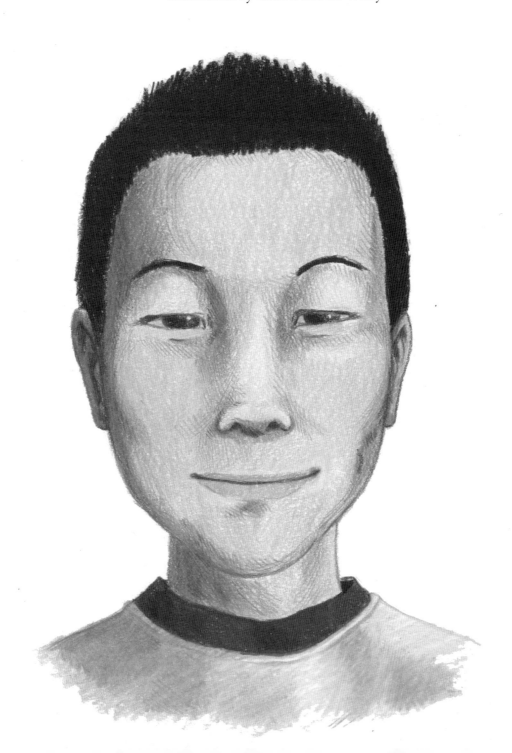

Chapter One | Trouble at Azuki Toys

"I'm so hungry," I said to Utada and Hotei as we walked past the restaurant at the end of our street. A plate of sashimi laid out in the window made my mouth water. It had been another long day, with regular school first and cram school after that. I reached into my black *randoseru* and found some sweet rice crackers to munch on. It wasn't sashimi, but it would have to do. "My stomach was rumbling so much I thought I wasn't going to make it through cram school," I said.

"How did you have time to think about food?" Hotei asked, raising an eyebrow. "Can you believe how much Sensei covered today? My hand hurts from writing so fast," he said.

"Come on, Hotei. You don't even have to write anything down," my cousin Utada said. "You remember it as soon as it comes out of Sensei's mouth."

Hotei crossed his arms. "Our middle school entrance exams are next month! All of us should be writing everything down," Hotei said. "What's the use of cram school if we don't try our best to pass the exams?"

I caught Utada's eye and we both shook our heads. Hotei is the smartest kid in our class, but he always worries about school anyway. Today in class he was holding his pencil so hard his knuckles were white. Utada and I grew up in Nagoya with Hotei, so we're used to his nervous habits.

"Want to meet here in the morning to walk to school?" I asked as we arrived at my house.

Hotei and Utada nodded. "See you tomorrow," they called.

Once through my front door, I stood in the *genkan* and took off my shoes. I was just about to call out that I was home when I heard Mom and Dad

talking in the kitchen. I paused next to the doorway. Dad's voice sounded dull, like he was very tired. Mom's voice didn't sound right either.

"Are you sure you added correctly?" she asked. "Or maybe a number is missing. Either way, it will be fine," she said quickly. I walked around the corner. As they saw me, they exchanged a glance.

"Hikaru, we didn't hear you come in," Mom said.

Dad slid some papers off the counter into a folder labeled "Azuki Toys." That was us—the Azukis, owners of Azuki Toys. Well, I'm not really the owner yet, but Dad says I will be someday. The shop is in the front room of our house, and I've been helping out there for years. When I first started, I hoped I'd get lots of toys, but that never happened. My mother always asked, "Hikaru, if you take all the toys, then what will we sell to the customers?"

Not long ago, a big new toy store opened across town. Lately, it seems like we don't have to worry about running out of toys to sell to the customers. We do seem to be running out of customers, though.

"Did you have a bad day at the store?" I asked.

Dad shrugged his shoulders. "For a Tuesday we did fine. That's what I was telling your mother." His face looked as though nothing was wrong, but his voice still sounded tired.

"I can work in the store after school for the rest of the week if you want," I offered. If I helped out, they wouldn't need to pay anyone to tidy up the store.

"No, no, no," Dad said immediately. "Cram school is far too important for you to skip. You help out more than enough on Saturdays."

"Besides," Mom said, "we'll be getting a shipment of Tiny Toys soon. Then I'm sure business will be great."

Tiny Toys! That's all anyone in school talks about—when they're not talking about exams. I saw one at a toy fair that looked like a little turtle. As soon as I tried it, I knew it would be a great seller. You can tell it to dance or walk or hop just by tapping it on the back.

That's what Azuki Toys needs, I thought. *A new toy or some other thing to make people notice us again. Something so cool that every kid will want to come here and buy our toys. But* . . . My stomach fluttered suddenly. I was sure the big toy store across town was going to sell Tiny Toys, too. Then what would happen? Now I knew why Dad seemed so worried.

Dad interrupted my thoughts. "I do have one thing you can help me with," he said. "We got another piece of mail that should have gone to Mrs. Takamaru. You can deliver it to her before dinner."

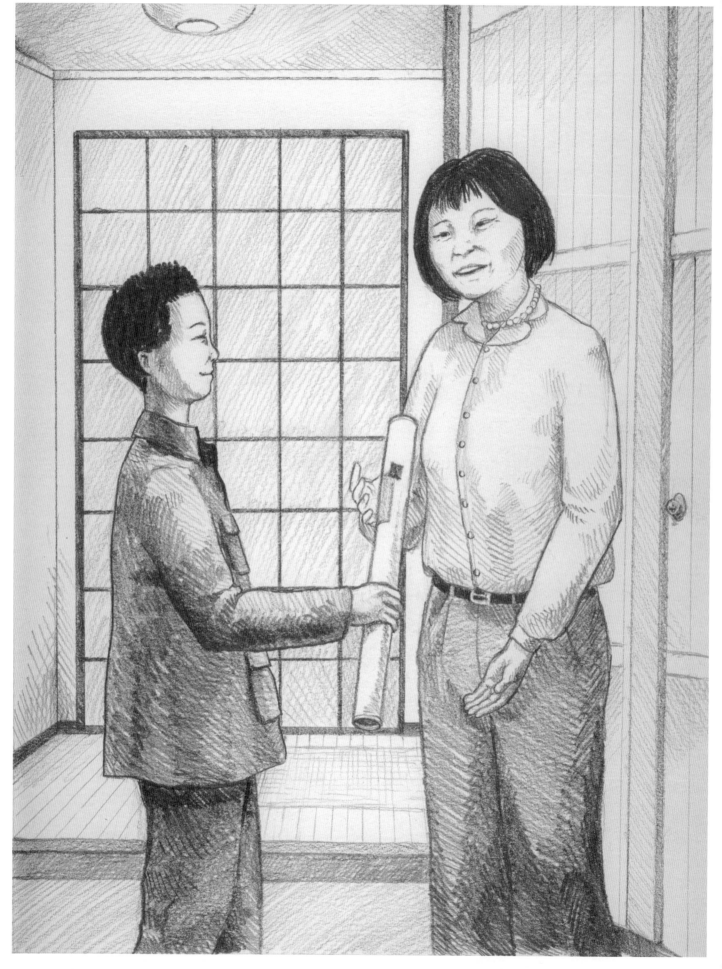

Chapter Two | Visiting Mrs. Takamaru

I wonder what's in the package, I thought, turning the cardboard tube over in my hands. As I got close to Mrs. Takamaru's door, the smell of *miso katsu* reached my nose. Thinking about the fried pork made my stomach rumble again. I worried for a moment that I might be interrupting her dinner. *She probably won't mind,* I decided, and knocked. I visit Mrs. Takamaru a lot. She tells me it's nice to have me around because all of her grandchildren live far away. Sometimes she comes over to dinner at our house and tells me folktales while Mom and Dad are cooking.

"Well, hello, Hikaru," Mrs. Takamaru said as she opened the door. "If I'd known you were stopping by, I would've made *wagashi* for you." I smiled. She knows I think her fancy little *wagashi* cakes are the best in Nagoya.

"It's okay," I said. "I haven't eaten dinner yet, anyway. Dad wanted me to bring you this." I handed her the package. "We got a piece of your mail again."

"Ah, just what I've been waiting for," she said. "Thank you for bringing it over."

"What is it?" I asked.

"It's blueprints for the project I'm working on. Would you like to take a look before you go?"

"Sure," I said. I took off my shoes and stepped inside.

I followed her across the *tatami* mat floor toward a low, square table in the living room with a blanket draped over the top. When I sat down, the heater under the *kotatsu* warmed my toes.

"Do you remember the train line that I worked on for the Expo fair? The Linimo line?"

"The maglev train? Of course! That was the best part of the fair!" For months the Expo fair had fascinated our town. Tourists came from all over Japan and even other places around the world—in part because you could take a floating magnetic train to get there! Mrs. Takamaru had helped design that train system. When I rode the train for the first time, she had come along and explained how the train worked. There were special magnets on the track that repelled, or pushed against, magnets on the bottom of the train. The force of repulsion was so great that the train floated above the tracks.

Mrs. Takamaru was always able to explain things in a way that made sense to me—things like her job, for instance. She's a transportation engineer. When I was younger, I thought Mrs. Takamaru drove trains for her job. But she

explained that train drivers are called engineers because they drive a vehicle with an engine. Transportation engineers like Mrs. Takamaru have a different type of job. They use their knowledge of science and math and their creativity to move things or people from place to place safely and efficiently. "Transportation engineers might help design trains," I remembered her saying, "but we probably wouldn't drive them."

"We're trying to improve the system for the Linimo line so it can move more people," Mrs. Takamaru now said, calling my attention back to the blueprints. "I'm working on the track system." Looking over her shoulder as she unrolled the blueprints, I saw the lines of the train tracks drawn on the papers.

Mrs. Takamaru turned to me. "Do you remember the transportation game we used to play when you were a little boy? How we would use all of your trucks and design a system to move your toys across the room as fast as we could?" I blushed a little, thinking about how babyish that was, but I did remember. "That was when I knew you'd love riding in the maglev train. I knew you were a transportation engineer at heart." She paused. "Now that the train line is old news, it's time for an upgrade."

"I guess things become less exciting as we get used to

them," I said, turning away from the blueprints. "Like my parents' store," I added under my breath.

Mrs. Takamaru placed a hand on my shoulder. "I think your parents' store is very exciting," Mrs. Takamaru said. "New technologies—and new stores like that big one across town—always make people take notice at first. I bet in a few months everything will return to normal."

New technologies make people take notice. I repeated the phrase in my head. *Can my parents wait a few months before customers notice them again?* I wondered.

"Well," Mrs. Takamaru said, "you should probably get back home before your dinner is cold."

On the walk back home I kept thinking about what Mrs. Takamaru had said. *New technologies make people take notice.* Maybe a new technology was the key to making Azuki Toys seem new and exciting again.

Chapter Three | Searching for an Idea

The next day I sat at my desk, staring at the classroom goal posted above the chalkboard: "Challenge yourself in new ways." Could helping my parents' store be my challenge?

I thought again about my conversation with Mrs. Takamaru the night before. *People get excited about new technologies. Like the Tiny Toys,* I thought. *The problem is, every store is getting Tiny Toys at the same time. What will make kids come to Azuki Toys instead of the big toy store across town? If there were another cool technology that only we had . . . like a robot bringing you the package after you buy it. Or a flying saucer to drive you around the toy store. Or . . .*

"Hikaru?" Uh oh. How long had Sensei been calling me?

"Yes?" I asked quietly.

"Yes?" he repeated in a stern voice. "Is that your answer?" I could only stare up at Sensei. "The correct answer is no." My face grew hot under his glare. "Hikaru, you haven't paid attention to a word I've said all morning. Stand in the back of the room for the rest of class. Then you may join your *han* for chores."

As I stood up, Utada caught my eye and smiled. It made me feel a little bit better.

After the lesson, Utada, Hotei, and I prepared food for lunch. We're part of a *han* group with a few other classmates. This week our group's chore was serving our class lunch. We'd been serving for a few minutes when Hotei approached me. "What were you thinking about, Hikaru?"

he asked. "Sensei was so mad. You're lucky you only had to stand in the back of the room."

"Chill out, Hotei," Utada said, coming up from behind me. "Everyone's practically forgotten about it already."

Hotei looked away and started to dish out the *miso* soup faster. "I was just curious," he said.

"I was going to tell you what I'd been thinking about, anyway," I said. I started to explain everything that had happened the night before, and my worries about Azuki Toys. Then I told them how I wanted to come up with a really exciting technology so everyone would buy Tiny Toys at my parents' store.

Utada spoke first. "I bet we can help you come up with an idea. I mean, think about it. You know more about toys than anyone else at school. And I know how to make things look cool and funky. And Hotei's just about the smartest person in the world," she said.

"That's not true," Hotei said. I thought I saw him blushing as he turned to serve more classmates. When he turned back, I could see a sparkle in his eyes, though, so I knew he was pleased with what Utada had said.

"With this team, we can't go wrong," Utada concluded. "We can think of ideas before cram school today."

"Wait," I said. "We need one more person—Mrs. Takamaru. Let's go to her house. I know she'll help us."

Chapter Four | An Attraction to Magnets

Sitting in Mrs. Takamaru's living room eating *wagashi*, Hotei, Utada, and I explained that we wanted to come up with an amazing technology to attract customers to Azuki Toys. Mrs. Takamaru listened carefully, but I couldn't tell what she was thinking.

"Do you think it's a good idea?" I asked, finally.

She smiled broadly. "I think it's great that you want to help your parents," she said. "And I think your idea of finding a way to attract customers to their store is a good one to explore."

"I can tell there's a 'but' coming," Utada said.

"Well, it's not a 'but,' exactly," Mrs. Takamaru said. "It's more like a 'first.' First, let's think about our definition

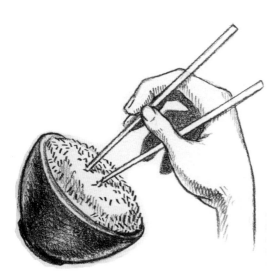

of technology. I like to think of technology as any thing or process that people create to help them solve a problem. So," she continued, "technology doesn't always have to be robots and computers. It might be something simple—like the chopsticks that help us eat or the shoes that protect our feet. What do you think of that?"

"I like your definition," I said. "We definitely have a problem to solve. And on the way here we already realized we might not have the money to buy something like a robot. A simple technology might be the best way to attract customers."

Utada scrunched up her nose. "But whatever we create can't be plain or boring. It has to be so great that people feel like they *have* to buy toys at Azuki Toys."

I could feel my brain getting cloudy, the way it sometimes does toward the end of cram school. How were we going to come up with something that was interesting and different, but not too expensive or too hard to do?

"Let me show you something," Mrs. Takamaru said, waving us over to the kitchen. "Last night Hikaru and I were talking about the Linimo line—the maglev train from the Expo fair. Did you both ride on that train, too?"

Utada and Hotei nodded. "The fair was great. And I've never been on a train as neat as the maglev train," Hotei said.

"I'm glad you think so!" Mrs. Takamaru said, smiling. "Now think about this. The main material that allowed us to design that train—the technology you all loved—was this." Mrs. Takamaru picked up two bar magnets from the top of her desk.

Hotei nodded. "I've read about how the Linimo line uses magnets to levitate the trains. May I?" he asked, nodding toward the two magnets. Mrs. Takamaru placed them in Hotei's hand.

"I love experimenting with magnets. Every magnet has two poles," he explained. "Opposite poles attract," he said, bringing the two magnets near each other until they stuck together with a click. "And like poles repel," he said, flipping one of the magnets over and trying to push them together. They remained a centimeter away from each other, not budging. "See," he said, "the like magnetic fields push the magnets apart."

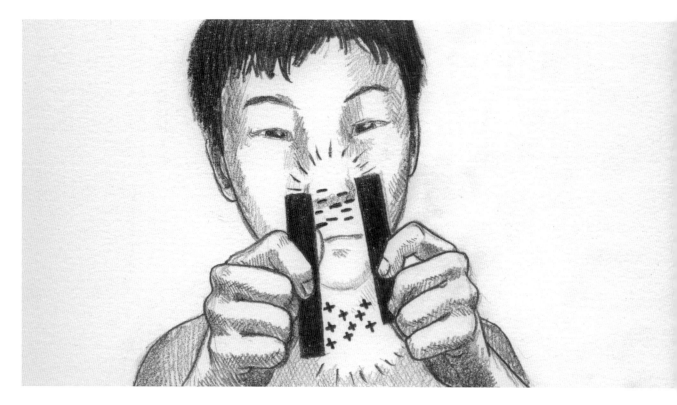

"Magnetic fields!" Utada piped up. "I remember learning about those in class. When we sprinkled little pieces of iron around a magnet, the iron lined up in rows."

"That's right," Mrs. Takamaru said. "A magnetic field is the space where the magnet has its effect. Magnets create magnetic forces within the magnetic field. We can use iron filings to reveal the forces."

"Transportation engineers must have to know a lot about magnets to design those trains," I said.

"We do," Mrs. Takamaru said. "But putting all that knowledge to work is worth it. Since the trains don't run on tracks, but float above them," Mrs. Takamaru explained, "they can move very quickly. We used the existing

technologies of magnets and train systems in a different way to create a technology that was new and helpful—not to mention exciting."

"I think the train is really cool," Utada said. "But how can we put these ideas to work at Azuki Toys?"

"That's what we have to focus on for the next few days," I said. "We have to take these ideas and rework them in a new way—just like Mrs. Takamaru did with the magnets for the Linimo line."

Mrs. Takamaru patted me on the shoulder. "That's a very good approach. I'm going to give you one more tool to use for your project. It's called the engineering design process. I use it to help me when I'm designing something new."

I saw Hotei's eyes light up. "I've never heard of the engineering design process," he said. "What is it?"

"It's a series of steps that help engineers solve problems. The first step is to ask good questions, just like you did with me today. Then you imagine possibilities for your design. That's what you need to do next—like Hikaru said. Then you make a detailed plan, and create your design to see how it works. Finally, you improve your design to make it the best it can be. That might mean starting the steps again, using all the new information you've gathered."

"And then we'll bring it to Azuki Toys to save the store!" I cried. Looking around at my design team, I knew we were going to be successful.

Chapter Five | Imagining the Possibilities

The next day, we met back at Mrs. Takamaru's house before cram school. We started working on the imagine step of our process. The problem was that none of us seemed to know where to start imagining. Robots and computers were too expensive, but everything else we could think of seemed boring.

"So we've already decided we need to do something new and different, right?" I said. "What Mrs. Takamaru did with magnets, that's new and different. Maybe we could do something with magnets, too—something as interesting as the maglev train."

"What if we had everything in the store floating around instead of sitting on shelves?" Utada suggested.

"In theory, we could do that," Hotei said, wrinkling his forehead. "We could make the whole floor of the store magnetic. Then we would have to figure out which toys or packages had magnetic properties—not all materials are magnetic, you know. If there were packages made of cardboard, for example, that weren't magnetic, we'd have to attach magnets to the bottom. And make sure the magnets on the box repelled the magnets on the floor, of course."

"Whoa, whoa. I think we're starting to think a little too big," I said. I could just imagine the looks on my parents' faces when they walked into our store with a magnetic floor and hundreds of floating toys—not to mention all the work it would take. "What if only the people who buy a toy get to see our special technology? Maybe it could be something that happens at the register?"

"I like that," Utada said. "That would get people to buy toys. Oh!" She snapped her fingers and leapt out of her chair. "Maybe once you buy something, your little package could levitate over to you. That would be some pretty cool technology."

I jumped up. "And people would need to buy something to see it float, so I bet sales really would go up!" I said. "But . . . " I sat down again. "How could we actually make this work?" The room got quiet. Finally Hotei came to the rescue.

"Mrs. Takamaru said that she made the maglev train float by putting it on a magnetic track," Hotei said. "I bet we could use the same idea. We could create a small magnetic track and then make a little magnetic train or vehicle that floats above it. Your package would ride on the vehicle and float to the end of the counter, where the customer would wait to pick it up. Maybe it could float right into a shopping bag!" Hotei sat back on his heels and crossed his arms, looking pretty proud of himself.

"It sounds amazing," I said. "But do you really think we can do it?"

"There's only one way to find out," Utada said. "What were those next steps Mrs. Takamaru mentioned? Plan and create? I think we should get to it."

Chapter Six	# Caught Up in the Excitement

After days of working on our plan and creating, testing, and improving our design, we finally had a model that worked. I looked across Mrs. Takamaru's living room at the pieces we'd designed. We built a track that would sit on the counter next to the cash register. When a customer bought a toy, the package would be placed on a vehicle that hovered over the track. With a little push, the vehicle would travel along the track and off the counter. Then, as an extra surprise, the vehicle would float into a shopping bag sitting on the floor, with help from a little parachute. Utada had come up with that idea. All we needed now was to make a few adjustments to be sure the track repelled the vehicle while a Tiny Toy was sitting on it.

I stood back and watched Hotei tinker with the track. "If we add just a few more magnets," he whispered to himself, "then the magnetic field should be strong enough." The tip of his tongue was sticking out of the corner of his mouth, and his forehead was wrinkled again. Utada was busy decorating the parachute for the package with calligraphy characters. The calligraphy was so nice that I almost felt bad poking holes in it to attach the strings.

"Okay, I think it's set," Hotei called. "How's the parachute coming?"

"Ready to go," Utada said. "Let's test it."

We carefully set the package on the small levitating vehicle. It hovered above the track, floating just as we had planned. Gently, Utada gave it a push. The package seemed to float effortlessly down the track. We all held our breath as it reached the end of the track and started to fall through the air.

"Look!" Utada cried. "It's working!" The little parachute she had designed helped the package drift gently to the ground, landing inside the Azuki Toys bag.

We all jumped around the room, shrieking at what we'd accomplished. Mrs. Takamaru came rushing in to share in our celebration. "May I see?" she asked.

"Of course!" Hotei said, setting up the maglev

platform. Utada adjusted the parachute and set the package in place.

"We present to you: the Maglev Package Transportation System!" I gave the vehicle a push, and again we watched the package float down the track and drift safely into the Azuki Toys bag. "I could do this all night!" I exclaimed.

Utada and Hotei settled on the ground and explained to Mrs. Takamaru all the tweaks we'd made to the track, and why we realized we needed a parachute to help the packages fall gently. I kept sending the package down the track, imagining how pleased Mom and Dad would be when

I got home from cram school and told them what we'd done. *Cram school!*

"Guys!" I said. "We forgot about cram school!" I frantically looked around the room for a clock. We were already almost an hour late. My eyes flew back to Hotei and Utada. Utada's eyes were big and her lips were clamped together, like she might cry. I could only imagine what Hotei was thinking—but when I looked at him, he seemed calm. He was still sitting by Mrs. Takamaru, not running to get his *randoseru* like I expected.

"It's okay, guys," he said. "It's just one day." I didn't know if I was more shocked by our forgetfulness or by Hotei's reaction. "Really," Hotei continued, looking at Utada's wide eyes. "I think our parents will understand when they see what we designed and how much we learned."

"I think Hotei is right," Mrs. Takamaru said. "I'm very impressed with how you used the engineering design process to solve your problem. I think your parents will be, too, but maybe you should all go home and explain what happened. You can leave everything set up here to show them."

I wasn't quite convinced. I walked to the door, still worried about the possibility of getting in big trouble. Huge trouble.

Chapter Seven | Facing Mom and Dad

I tiptoed into the *genkan* and quietly closed the door behind me. *Maybe if they don't hear me come in, they won't even realize I'm home early and that I skipped cram school—*

"Hikaru!" My mother's voice echoed from the doorway. "I just got off the phone with your cram school. You have some serious explaining to do."

I walked into the living room and looked at Dad. He didn't even seem mad. It was worse—he looked disappointed.

I stifled the urge to start off, "I can explain." Instead I said, "I'm sorry."

Dad was quiet for a few moments. "I'm sorry, too," he said finally. "I can't believe that you skipped cram school, knowing how important it is—to you, and to your family."

"I know," I said, nodding my head. "It's just that . . . well, I didn't mean to skip it."

"What do you mean, you didn't mean to?" Mom asked, hands on her hips.

"Hotei and Utada and I have been working on a special project with Mrs. Takamaru. And we lost track of time," I said nervously. Mom and Dad were both staring at me, not saying anything.

Finally Dad sighed and asked, "What kind of project?"

I took the question as a good sign. "Maybe I can show it to you?" I suggested.

Mom and Dad exchanged a long glance before they turned to me and agreed. Before I knew it, we were standing in front of Mrs. Takamaru's house, waiting for her to open the door.

Chapter Eight | The Maglev Package Transportation System

When we walked into the living room, I was surprised to see Hotei and Utada there with their parents, too. I guess we really were all in the same mess.

"Go on, Hikaru," Mrs. Takamaru said. "We've all been waiting for you to demonstrate what you three have been working on."

My palms were sweaty as I picked up the vehicle. Maybe this wasn't such a super idea. What if my parents thought it was silly? That we'd been goofing off? "Well, um . . . " I stammered and gulped.

"Well!" Utada exclaimed, jumping up to stand next to me. She threw her arms out wide. "Ladies and gentlemen! We present to you a highly imaginative technology to solve a BIG problem."

"Yes—a problem," I said. "As you know, a new store has come to town and has been drawing customers from Azuki Toys." Dad raised an eyebrow, but I continued. "So we decided to create a cutting-edge technology to attract customers back to Azuki Toys. We designed a Maglev Package Transportation System to move purchases from the register right into shopping bags. Customers will be thrilled by this new technology. They'll keep coming back and buying more toys to see it again!"

With a nudge from me, the package floated down the track and into the Azuki Toys bag. The three of us stood quietly, waiting for our parents' reactions.

Dad picked up the vehicle and placed it back on the track. Then he brought his face really close to the track and pressed down on the vehicle. It sprang back up into the air,

returning to its floating position. I wasn't sure what to do in the silence, so I started talking again.

"We learned all about magnets—that all magnets have poles, and like poles repel, and what magnetic fields are, and that some materials are magnetic and others are not . . ." I trailed off, desperately waiting for Dad to say something.

"You kids made all this by yourself?" Dad asked.

"Well, we had help from Mrs. Takamaru," I explained. "I came up with the first idea, Hotei improved the track, and Utada designed the parachute."

Hotei's mom started clapping, and all the other adults joined in. "I love it!" Dad said. "Azuki Toys will never be the same!"

"So you'll really use it in the store?" Utada asked.

"Of course we will," Mom said.

| Chapter Nine | # The True Test |

Two Saturdays later I walked out of school and met Hotei and Utada on the steps. "How did it go?" Hotei asked. We'd just finished our huge middle school entrance exam.

"I think it went all right," I said. "But the real test hasn't happened yet. The real test starts now."

"Right," Utada said. "The debut of Tiny Toys and the Maglev Package Transportation System!"

"Well, let's head over to Azuki Toys to check it out," Hotei said.

....

As we turned onto my street, I saw lots of people walking around. "Excuse me, sorry," I said, weaving through the crowd. Then I saw Mom walking toward me.

"Hikaru!" she called. "Come quickly! We have a big problem."

My heart sank. "A big problem?" I asked.

"Yes," she said. "There's been a steady stream of customers at the register all day. I need you to help watch the store. Your design has attracted so many people that we're nearly sold out of Tiny Toys already. I need to go to the warehouse to pick up some more."

Hotei and Utada each gave me a big smile. If we had to have a problem, this one wasn't so bad!

"I guess our technology is a success!" Hotei said.

"It sure is," Utada said. "But we shouldn't stop here. Maybe we could design a display for the store window. Or an easier way to stock the shelves."

"I have an idea," I said with a smile. "How about an alarm to remind us when it's time for cram school?"

Utada and Hotei laughed. "Now that sounds like a good place to start!" Utada said.

I grinned as we walked into the store and saw the technology we'd designed sitting on the counter—and the crowds of people filling the aisles. With a little creativity and some great engineering, Azuki Toys was new and exciting again!

Design a Maglev System

Can you design a maglev transportation system like Hikaru and his friends? Your goal is to create a track and vehicle that can move pennies, crayons, or pencils from one place to another.

Materials
☐ A bar magnet with poles marked
☐ Small paper cup
☐ Pennies or other small objects
☐ A pen
☐ Masking tape
☐ Sheets of cardboard
☐ A box that is about one foot long and three or four inches wide
☐ Magnets of different shapes and sizes (try to get some disc or bar shaped magnets, and a few feet of strip magnets)

Experiment With Your Magnets
To figure out where the poles are on your magnet, notice whether the marked bar magnet repels or attracts different areas of the other magnets. Like poles repel and opposite poles attract. Use pieces of masking tape and a pen to mark the poles of the other magnets as either north or south. What part of your design should repel? Are there any parts that should attract?

Design a Track and Vehicle
Your track will be designed so it fits in the bottom of the box. Imagine which magnets you might use to create your track. Think about how they need to be placed so that they will repel a vehicle. Once you've come up with a plan, build your track in the box.

Your vehicle needs to levitate over the track. How should you place the magnets on your vehicle so it levitates? What shape magnets should you use? Create a plan for your vehicle and then build it!

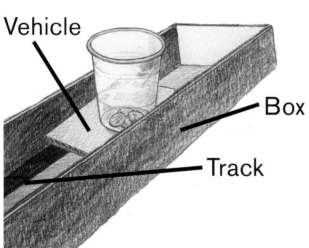

Vehicle

Box

Track

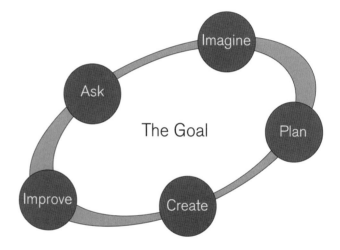

Imagine

Ask

The Goal

Plan

Improve

Create

Test Your System!

Does your vehicle levitate over your track? If you give it a push, can your vehicle float down the track from one end of the box to the other without tipping over? You may need to improve your system by adding or removing some magnets so your system is stable.

Place a small paper cup on top of your vehicle so you can carry pennies or whatever other objects you've decided to transport. How many objects can your vehicle carry while it levitates?

Improve Your Maglev System

Use the engineering design process to improve your maglev system. Can you create a vehicle that levitates higher? Can you make your system more efficient so you can transport more pennies?

Glossary

Cram school: A private school that offers lessons after the normal school day and on weekends in order to help prepare students for school entrance exams.

Engineer: A person who uses his or her creativity and understanding of mathematics and science to design things that solve problems.

Engineering design process: The steps that engineers use to design something to solve a problem.

***Genkan*:** Japanese word for the entryway of a home, where guests' shoes can be removed before they enter the house. Pronounced *gen-CAN*.

***Han* group:** A small group of students who work together to perform classroom chores and school management tasks. Pronounced *hahn*.

***Kotatsu*:** Japanese word for a low table with a small heater underneath. It is usually covered with a blanket and used to keep feet warm. Pronounced *co-TAT-soo*.

Levitate: To rise or float in the air.

Maglev train: A train that uses the magnetic force of repulsion to levitate, or float, above a track.

Magnet: An object that attracts iron and is surrounded by a magnetic field.

Miso katsu: Dish for which the city of Nagoya is well-known. Miso is a soy paste that is made into a sweet sauce and poured over katsu (fried pork cutlets). Pronounced *MEE-so COT-soo.*

Randoseru: Japanese word for backpack. Pronounced *RON-doe-ser-oo.*

Repel: To push away with an opposing force.

Sashimi: Japanese cuisine made from very fresh, thinly sliced fish. Pronounced *sa-SHE-mee.*

Sensei: Japanese word for teacher. Pronounced *SEN-say.*

Tatami: Woven straw mats that are used as traditional Japanese flooring. Pronounced *tuh-TAH-mee.*

Technology: Any thing, system, or process that people create and use to solve a problem.

Transportation engineer: Someone who uses what he or she knows about science, math, safety, and efficiency to design systems that move objects or people from place to place.

Wagashi: Traditional Japanese sweets that are served during tea ceremonies. Pronounced *wuh-GAH-she.*